CU00842813

For Oscar and Ruairi
and everyone else...

Who is my

Angel ?

First published in United Kingdom in 2003 by
McCrimmon Publishing Co. Ltd.,
Great Wakering, Essex, SS3 0EQ
info@mccrimmons.com
www.mccrimmons.com

ISBN 0 85597 641 1

With thanks to: Liz Mellon, John O'Leary, Julie Aldridge,
Margaret Hardman, Aidan Tarbett, Bill Nolan and Dee Byers for
their help and encouragement.

Typeset in ITC Kristen Normal, 16pt
Printed and bound by Fuller-Davies Ltd., Ipswich, Suffolk   G/0F

Who is my Angel ?

Barbara Nolan

McCrimmons
Great Wakering, Essex, United Kingdom

Your angel's your mate
Your very best friend,
Born to stick by you
From beginning to end.

Your angel is there
When you wake up each day,
Saying "Go have some fun
But keep danger at bay".

When you are learning
To run and play ball,
Your angel tries hard
To soften your fall.

Angels like playing
And making a mess,
Doing things YOU like
That grown-ups like less.

Your angel is able
To send monsters away,
And bad witches and ghosts
Who think they can stay.

If you're having a party
Your angels come too,
And the ones who pig out
Are the angels... that's who!

When you're doing a jig-saw
And can't find the right bit,
Your angel can help
Find the piece that will fit

Sometimes when you're sick
And can't ride your bike,
Your angel will mind you,
Watch TV if you like.

Some angels lie cosy
Beside you in bed,
Some keep you from harm
At your feet or your head.

There's all sorts of angels
Some with wings, some without
Some swoop by like a rainbow
Dancing brightly about.

Most people can't see them
But they help us feel tall,
Legions of angels
Guarding us all.

Doesn't it feel good
Now that you know,
Where-ever you are
You are never alone.